CONTENTS

ACKNOWLEDGMENTS

'Windy Nights' by Rodney Bennett is reprinted by permission of Mrs J R Bennett; 'Mud' by Polly Chase Boyden by permission of Mrs Barbara B Jordan; 'There are big waves' by Eleanor Farjeon, and 'Conjuror', 'Conkers', 'The Roundabout' and 'The Engine Driver' from *The Golden Unicorn* by Clive Sansom by permission of David Higham Associates Ltd; 'Ducks' Ditty' from *The Wind in the Willows* by Kenneth Grahame, published by Methuen's Children's Books, by permission of Associated Book Publishers Ltd (text copyright University Chest Oxford) and Charles Scribner's Sons (copyright 1908 Charles Scribner's Sons); 'Sink Song' by permission of Mr J A Lindon; 'Daddy fell into the pond' and 'The moon is up' by Alfred Noyes by permission of William Blackwood & Sons Ltd; 'Fireworks' from *The Blackbird in the Lilac* by permission of Oxford University Press; 'Under ground' by James Reeves from *The Wandering Moon* by permission of William Heinemann Ltd; 'White Fields' from *Collected Poems* by James Stephens by permission of Mrs Iris Wise, Macmillan London & Basingstoke, The Macmillan Company of Canada Ltd, and Macmillan Publishing Co Inc New York; 'The Policeman' by Jan Struther by permission of *Punch*; 'The Arrival' by John Walsh from *The roundabout by the sea* by permission of Mrs A M Walsh; 'Have you ever?' by permission of Mr Peter Young.

chosen by Audrey Daly

illustrated by James Hodgson

HAVE YOU EVER?

Have you ever stood on your head
had a pillow fight in bed
rolled over and over down a slope
climbed and swung from a piece of rope
jumped around on a pogo pole
dug yourself a big, deep hole
swung to and fro on five-barred gates
roared around on roller skates

flown a kite
stayed up all night
ridden a donkey, ridden a horse
traced a river to its sourc
fallen over and cut your
swum down to the bottom of the ea—
have you

?

THE MOON

The moon has a face like the clock
in the hall;
She shines on thieves on the garden wall,
On streets and fields and harbour quays,
And birdies asleep in the forks
of the trees.

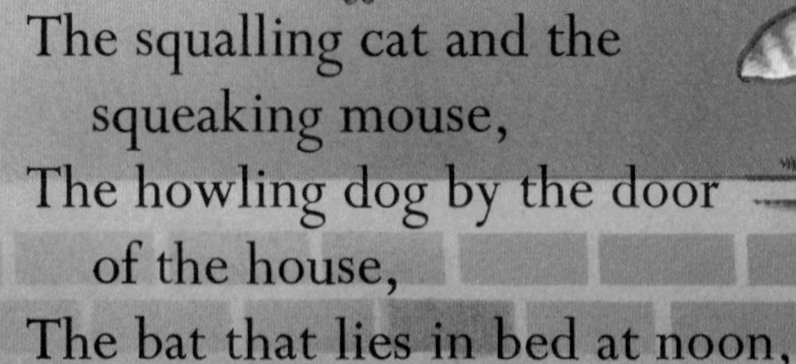

The squalling cat and the
squeaking mouse,
The howling dog by the door
of the house,
The bat that lies in bed at noon,
All love to be out by the light
of the moon.

But all of the things that belong to the day
Cuddle to sleep to be out of her way;
And flowers and children close their eyes
Till up in the morning the sun shall rise.

Robert Louis Stevenson

THE ENGINE DRIVER

The train goes running along the line,
Jicketty-can, jicketty-can.
I wish it were mine, I wish it were mine,
Jicketty-can, jicketty-can.
The Engine Driver stands in front—
He makes it run, he makes it shunt;

Out of the town,
Out of the town,
Over the hill,
Over the down,
Under the bridges,
Across the lea,
Over the bridges
And down to the sea,

With a jicketty-can, jicketty-can,
Jicketty-jicketty-jicketty-can,
Jicketty-can, jicketty-can . . .

Clive Sansom

MUD

Mud is very nice to feel
All squishy-squash between the toes!
I'd rather wade in wiggly mud
Than smell a yellow rose.

Nobody else but the rosebush knows
How nice mud feels
Between the toes.

Polly C. Boyden

BLOCK CITY

What are you able to build with your blocks?
Castles and palaces, temples and docks.
Rain may keep raining, and others go roam,
But I can be happy and building at home.

Let the sofa be mountains, the carpet be sea,
There I'll establish a city for me:
A kirk and a mill and a palace beside,
And a harbour as well where my vessels may ride.

Great is the palace with pillar and wall,
A sort of a tower on top of it all,
And steps coming down in an orderly way
To where my toy vessels lie safe in the bay.

This one is sailing and that one is moored:
Hark to the song of the sailors on board!
And see on the steps of my palace, the kings
Coming and going with presents and things!

Now I have done with it, down let it go!
All in a moment the town is laid low.
Block upon block lying scattered and free,
What is there left of my town by the sea?

Yet as I saw it, I see it again,
The kirk and the palace, the ships and the main,
And as long as I live and where'er I may be,
I'll always remember my town by the sea.

Robert Louis Stevenson

THERE ARE BIG WAVES

There are big waves and little waves,
Green waves and blue,
Waves you can jump over,
Waves you dive through.

Waves that rise up
Like a great water wall,
Waves that swell softly
And don't break at all.

Waves that can whisper,
Waves that can roar,
And tiny waves that run at you
Running on the shore.

Eleanor Farjeon

THE ROUNDABOUT

Round and round the roundabout,
Down the 'slippery stair'—
I'm always to be found about
When the circus men are there.
The music of the roundabout,
The voices in the air,
The horses as they pound about,
The boys who shout and stare—
There's such a lovely sound about
A circus or a fair.

Clive Sansom

THE ARRIVAL

Our train steams slowly in,
and we creep to a stop at last.
There's a great unlatching of doors,
and the coaches, emptying fast,
Let loose their loads of children,
and mothers with talkative friends,
And sandwiches, flasks and push-chairs,
and apples, and odds and ends.

And we move in a crowd together,
amid churns and trolleys and crates,
Along by a cobbled courtyard,
and out through the station gates;
We pass by the waiting taxis;
then turn a corner and reach
To where with its flags and cafés
the road curves down to the beach.

We move in the livelier air,
  between shining shops and stalls;
Never was such a confusion of coloured,
  bright beach-balls,
And plastic buckets and boats,
  and ducks of a rubbery blue,
And strings of sandals,
  and stacks of rock-with-the-name-right-through!

Till the many smells which beset us —
  of onions and cooking greens,
Of fumes from the cars and buses,
  of smoke from the noisy inns —
All merge in the one large gust
  which blows on us broad and free,
And catches us, throat, and limbs, and heart —
  the smell of the sea!

John Walsh

THE POLICEMAN

Every few hours
Throughout the night
He comes to see
That the Square is all right.
Slowly and solemnly
Round he goes
On his great flat feet
With their great blunt toes,
Shifting his very
Portentous weight
From side to side
With a rolling gait.
He flashes his lantern
Up and down;
His brows are bent
In an ominous frown;
To see him you'd think
No thief would dare
To crack a crib
In Sycamore Square.

Yet when he's at home
You'll probably find
He's a jovial man
And extremely kind,
Who likes his pint
And a kipper for tea
The same as you—
Or, at any rate, me.

Jan Struther

WINDY NIGHTS

Rumbling in the chimneys,
Rattling at the doors,
Round the roofs and round the roads
The rude wind roars;
Raging through the darkness,
Raving through the trees,
Racing off again across
The great grey seas.

Rodney Bennett

DUCKS' DITTY

All along the backwater,
Through the rushes tall,
Ducks are a-dabbling,
Up tails all!

Ducks' tails, drakes' tails,
Yellow feet a-quiver,
Yellow bills all out of sight
Busy in the river!

Slushy green undergrowth
Where the roach swim—
Here we keep our larder,
Cool and full and dim!

Everyone for what he likes!
We like to be
Heads down, tails up,
Dabbling free!

High in the blue above
Swifts whirl and call—
We are down a-dabbling
Up tails all!

Kenneth Grahame

UNDER GROUND

In the deep kingdom under ground
There is no light and little sound.

Down below the earth's green floor
The rabbit and the mole explore.

The quarrying ants run to and fro
To make their populous empires grow.

Do they, as I pass overhead,
Stop in their work to hear my tread?

Some creatures sleep and do not toil,
Secure and warm beneath the soil.

Sometimes a fork or spade intrudes
Upon their earthy solitudes.

Downward the branching tree-roots spread
Into the country of the dead.

Deep down, the buried rocks and stones
Are like the earth's gigantic bones.

In the dark kingdom under ground
How many marvellous things are found!

James Reeves

THE LAND OF COUNTERPANE

When I was sick and lay a-bed,
I had two pillows at my head,
And all my toys beside me lay
To keep me happy all the day.

And sometimes for an hour or so
I watched my leaden soldiers go,
With different uniforms and drills,
Among the bed-clothes, through
the hills;

And sometimes sent my ships in fleets
All up and down among the sheets;
Or brought my trees and houses out,
And planted cities all about.

I was the giant great and still
That sits upon the pillow-hill,
And sees before him, dale and plain,
The pleasant land of counterpane.

Robert Louis Stevenson

DADDY FELL INTO THE POND

Everyone grumbled. The sky was grey.
We had nothing to do and nothing to say
We were nearing the end of a dismal day,
And there seemed to be nothing beyond,
THEN
Daddy fell into the pond!

And everyone's face grew
merry and bright,
And Timothy danced for sheer delight.
"Give me the camera, quick, oh quick!
He's crawling out of the duckweed."
Click!

Then the gardener suddenly
slapped his knee,
And he doubled up, shaking silently,
And the ducks all quacked
as if they were daft
And it sounded as if the old drake laughed.

O, there wasn't a thing that didn't respond
WHEN
Daddy fell into the pond!

Alfred Noyes

CONKERS

When chestnuts are hanging
Above the school yard,
They are little green sea-mines
Spiky and hard.

But when they fall bursting
And all the boys race,
Each shines like a jewel
In a satin case.

Clive Sansom

SAMPAN

Waves lap lap
Fish fins clap clap
Brown sails flap flap
Chop-sticks tap tap;

Up and down the long green river,
Oh hey, oh hey, lanterns quiver,
Willow branches brush the river,
Oh hey, oh hey, lanterns quiver.

Chop-sticks tap tap
Brown sails flap flap
Fish fins clap clap
Waves lap lap.

Anon.

AUTUMN FIRES

In the other gardens
    And all up the vale,
From the autumn bonfires
    See the smoke trail!

Pleasant summer over
    And all the summer flowers,
The red fire blazes,
    The grey smoke towers.

Sing a song of seasons!
    Something bright in all!
Flowers in the summer,
    Fires in the fall!

Robert Louis Stevenson

WHERE GO THE BOATS?

Dark brown is the river,
　Golden is the sand.
It flows on for ever,
　With trees on either hand.

Green leaves a-floating,
　Castles of the foam,
Boats of mine a-boating—
　Where will all come home?

On goes the river
　　And out past the mill,
Away down the valley,
　　Away down the hill.

Away down the river,
　　A hundred miles or more,
Other little children
　　Shall bring my boats ashore.

Robert Louis Stevenson

FIREWORKS

They rise like sudden fiery flowers
  That burst upon the night,
Then fall to earth in burning showers
  Of crimson, blue, and white.

Like buds too wonderful to name,
  Each miracle unfolds,
And catherine-wheels begin to flame
  Like whirling marigolds.

Rockets and Roman candles make
  An orchard of the sky,
Whence magic trees their petals shake
  Upon each gazing eye.

James Reeves

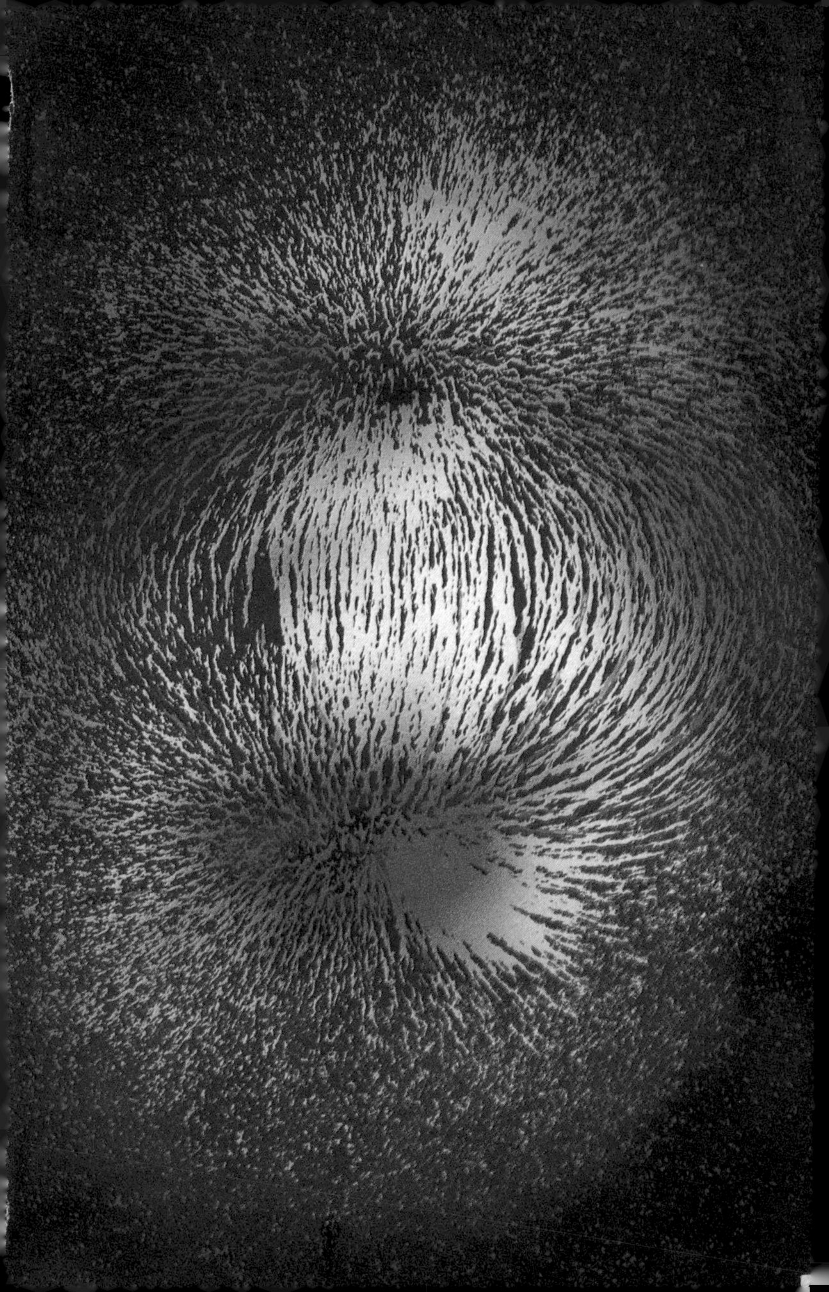

WHITE FIELDS

In the winter time we go
Walking in the fields of snow;

Where there is no grass at all;
Where the top of every wall,

Every fence, and every tree
Is as white as white can be.

Pointing out the way we came—
Every one of them the same—

All across the fields there be
Prints in silver filigree;

And our mothers always know,
By the footprints in the snow,

Where it is the children go.

James Stephens

SINK SONG

Scouring out the porridge pot,
    Round and round and round!

Out with all the scraith and scoopery.
Lift the eely ooly droopery,
Chase the glubbery slubbery gloopery
    Round and round and round!

Out with all the doleful dithery,
Ladle out the slimy slithery,
Hunt and catch the hithery thithery,
　　Round and round and round!

Out with all the obbly gubbly,
On the stove it burns so bubbly,
Use the spoon and use it doubly,
　　Round and round and round!

J. A. Lindon

CONJUROR

He takes an empty hat —
Like that —
Raps it . . . taps it . . .
And out pops a rabbit
in a large pink bow!
How does he do it?
How *does* he do it?
How does he *do* it?
I would like to know.

He takes an old stick —
Just a trick —
Raps it . . . taps it . . .
And there's a string of coloured flags
all in a row!
How does he do it?
How *does* he do it?
How does he *do* it?
I would like to know.

He takes a small book —
Now look!
Raps it . . . taps it . . .
Changes it to turtle-doves and
lets them all go!
How does he do it?
How *does* he do it?
How does he *do* it?
I would like to know.

Clive Sansom

THE MOON IS UP

The moon is up. The stars are bright.
The wind is fresh and free.
We're out to seek for gold tonight
Across the silver sea.
The world was growing grey and old:
Break out the sails again!
We're out to seek a Realm of Gold
Beyond the Spanish Main.

We're sick of all the cringing knees,
The courtly smiles and lies.
God, let Thy singing Channel breeze
Lighten our hearts and eyes!
Let love no more be bought and sold
For earthly loss or gain.
We're out to seek an Age of Gold
Beyond the Spanish Main.

Beyond the light of far Cathay,
Beyond all mortal dreams,
Beyond the reach of night and day
Our El Dorado gleams,
Revealing — as the skies unfold —
A star without a stain,
The Glory of the Gates of Gold
Beyond the Spanish Main.

Alfred Noyes